DON'T BE THAT KID!™
AT SCHOOL

Lois McGuire

TELEMACHUS PRESS

Don't Be That Kid!™ is a Trademark of Lois McGuire

Cover and interior art by Jorge Pacheco

Visit the author website: www.dontbethatkid.net

Published by: Telemachus Press, LLC

Visit our website: http://www.telemachuspress.com

ISBN# 978-1-942899-69-3 (eBook)

ISBN# 978-1-942899-70-9 (Hardback)

Library of Congress Control Number: 2016953461

Printed in the United States of America

10 9 8 7 6 5 4 3 2 1

Version: 2016.09.25

Don't Be That KID!™ At School is dedicated in memory of my parents, Jack and Lorna Podolsky, who encouraged me to work in the field of education.

The book and resource guide would never have been accomplished without the collaboration, patience and love of my family: Steve & Ellen Podolsky, Scott, Amy, Josh & Danny Podolsky, Alan, Alison, Rutger & Lailani Doe, and my husband Jim.

3

SCHOOL BUS

When riding to school
stay seated on the bus

4

DON'T BE THAT KID!
Who causes a fuss

5

Paint is for paper
Not desks, walls or your face

DON'T BE THAT KID!
Who makes a mess of the place

DON'T BE THAT KID!
Who rips out the pages

DON'T BE THAT KID!
Who just leaves the tray

Hitting a classmate just isn't right

20

33

35

Lois McGuire
Author

Lois McGuire has 35 years of teaching and leadership experience in the field of education. She began her career as a 4th and 5th grade teacher and retired as the Superintendent of Schools of a highly acclaimed K – 12 school district in New Jersey.

Lois has a strong record of accomplishment in the areas of instructional supervision, curriculum development/direction, personnel issues at all levels, public relations, budgeting, facilities and grant writing. She received many honors as an educator including being awarded seven Best Practices Awards by the New Jersey Department of Education, nine Awards of Excellence from New Jersey School Boards and the New Jersey Coalition of Educational Leaders Award for Outstanding Service and Leadership. She was selected to join New Jersey Governor Thomas Kean at the Governor's Conference in Cincinnati to discuss youth-at-risk. She has been a consultant to the U.S. Department of Education and the N.J. Department of Education on such topics as parent involvement in the schools, career development for children, character education, positive communication skills and strategic planning.

Lois earned her Doctorate in Education from Rutgers University. She was an adjunct professor at Rutgers, Bloomfield College and St. Peter's College where she taught courses in the areas of education, psychology and human relations.

Lois presently lives in Florida with her husband, Jim. She wrote Don't Be That KID! At School and the Don't Be That KID! At School Resource Guide to help educators and parents guide their children through the maze of building essential positive character traits.

Please visit her website at: www.dontbethatkid.net

Jorge Pacheco
Illustrator

Jorge Pacheco has been a professional illustrator for the past 30 years. He has illustrated several children's books including the one you are holding in your hands. Mr.Pacheco has worked for almost every major Comic Book company including Dark Horse Comics, DC Comics, IDW Comics and Archie Comics. Mr. Pacheco was staff artist for Harvey Comics/Entertainment and has drawn many famous licensed characters, such as Casper the friendly Ghost, The Flintstones, Bullwinkle and Rocky, Angry Birds and he even worked briefly for Jim (Garfield) Davis. He also had his own syndicated cartoon strip CEO Dad. Mr. Pacheco has spoken at both the Chuck Jones Center for Creativity & the Charles M. Schulz Museum and Research Center. Mr. Pacheco would like to dedicate this book to his wonderful children, Jonas-Jorge (J.J.) and Lizzie Pacheco. Please check out Mr. Pacheco's website for even more about him.www.pachecotoons.com

CPSIA information can be obtained
at www.ICGtesting.com
Printed in the USA
BVHW021912270720
584797BV00006B/27